AUTHORIZED
AUTUMN
CHARTS
OF THE
UPPER RED
CANOE RIVER
COUNTRY

AUTHORIZED
AUTUMN
CHARTS

OF THE

UPPER RED
CANOE RIVER
COUNTRY

PETER ZACHARY COHEN

Illustrated by Tomie de Paola

Atheneum 1972 New York

For Todd,
who should be ready
to travel with Jay

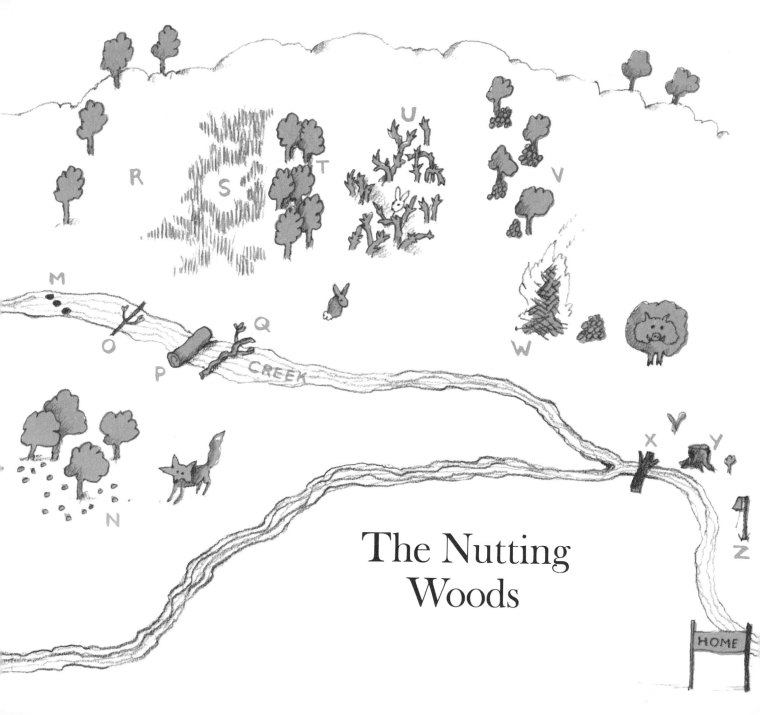

The Nutting
Woods

When the time comes in autumn to begin storing food for winter, drift by canoe downstream to the wide pool in the river (A). Leave the canoe and take with you a tranquilizer gun and a burlap sack. If it's rainy, also bring along a long-handled fishnet. Work *quietly* up the embankment at (B) to the higher land thick with juniper trees.

Go very carefully into the jumble of blown-down junipers (C) until there is a good view of the open den (D) of the wild boar who feeds by night on the fallen walnuts and on the surrounding fields.

E

D

Shoot the resting boar with a sleeping pill from the tranquilizer gun to be sure he doesn't waken and bother you. If your shot misses, hurriedly slide down the embankment at (E) and run to the canoe, which will have drifted downstream to the river's elbow bend (F), and come again some other day.

F

If your sleeping pill shot is successful, relax
ten minutes among the junipers, then wander
on through them and climb to the top of the
walnut tree ridge (G). At midmorning you
will be able to look out through the trees and
see squirrels feeding down below in the field of
milo (H).

Resist the temptation to pick the walnuts on the ridge and run down it—*making lots of noise*—to point (I). The squirrels will hear you and run to the trees that are farthest away from you: the sycamore (J) and oak (K) trees along the little creek. They will jump through the sycamore and oak trees to reach the walnut tree ridge (G) where their homes are.

You should run to point (L). If you come on a rainy day, you will not only see the squirrels leaping over you, but many squirrels will lose their footing on the slippery sycamores and sail into the thick autumn leaves at your feet. You can then chase after them and catch them with the long-handled fishnet.

Don't try to keep any caught squirrel for long, or the squirrel will be badly frightened and the net will be badly torn. When the last squirrel has jumped free, cross the little creek at the stepping stones (M) and begin to fill the burlap sack with walnuts from the walnut woods (N)

When the burlap sack is as full as you want to carry, cross back over the little creek on the thin, fallen log (O), or on the thick, fallen log (P) or along the twisty, fallen log (Q).

R

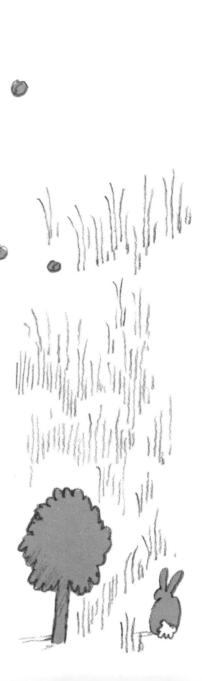

Then go to the playing field (R) opposite to the thickly-grassed pasture (S). At the field you can begin playing bat-and-catch, with the walnuts as balls; also, slingshot and target games, with the walnuts as bullets; and any other games you can think of that will help wear the hulls off the nuts. If you have brought a few friends with you, you will be able to play many different kinds of games and hull many walnuts.

s

Take the hulled walnuts to the edge of the woods (T) and leave them where squirrels will easily find them. This will pay the squirrels for leaping through the trees for you, and make up for interrupting their food gathering.

After that try to find your way through the rabbit briar (U) without getting lost, without having to back up and without disturbing any rabbits. The person who comes through first, and startles the fewest rabbits from their nests, gets first pick of walnuts at every tree in walnut woods (V). If you've come alone, you are sure to be the winner.

Now build a fire and roast the walnuts from these woods (V) at point (W).

When you've eaten enough, and rested enough, and have watched the winkling waters of the little creek long enough and have listened long enough to its musical bubbling;

when you've put out the fire and made the campsite look fresh again, and gathered up the fishnet and tranquilizer gun and the burlap sack with the walnuts you'll want to keep: follow the little creek back to the river, near the long, heavy tree trunk (X) lying across it. The canoe will have drifted downstream and lodged against the tree trunk.

Portage the empty canoe around the trunk, and when it is back in the water tie it to the old stump (Y) and reload it. When you are done, it should be nearly evening.

Go back and ring the old woodland school bell (Z) to wake up the sleeping boar for his suppertime. Then get back in the canoe, untie it and drift on downstream to where someone will meet you and help you store the nuts away.

DUCKS

The Oxbow
Expedition

To begin being a river pilot, start on an early fall day, and in midmorning beach your canoe at the river's oxbow cove (A) and set up your tent and bedding on the nearby knoll (B). The river used to bend around the knoll into a long oxbow curve and gradually it wore the oxbow's "horns" together and cut across them, as rivers usually do. Some water still flows through the curve, but a canoe can no longer follow. So take the bullboat and its paddle from a platform on the new point-of-land (C).

The bullboat is a cup-shaped frame of willows covered by a big hide with the hair side out. Fleas will have gathered in the hair to lay eggs. Check to be sure they are there. You should not begin without them. When you do

begin, float the bullboat in the boggy entrance
(D) to the old curve, and step carefully aboard
with the paddle. At first the bullboat will drift
on the current into the flea fish furrows.

The furrows are still slowly changing as the
current washes in new sand and mud and
gouges out new channels. As you choose your
way from one furrow to the next, watch for the
bright blue flea fish that will rise to nibble at
the flea larvae. The flea fish live only in the
fresh, new currents, so if you stop seeing their
bright blue flashes beside you, paddle back
right away and try another furrow, or you will
become endlessly lost in the old ones.

As you go further, the water will slow down and you'll have to paddle to keep the bullboat moving. When the flea fish flickerings stop in the middle of a long southward furrow (E), you'll soon see the first hard point of the rip-rock rings.

Ahead the water begins passing around eight rocky islands. Some of these passages are filled with sharp rocks, dangerous to the boat. Yet the water moves so slowly and smoothly you can see no warning ripples. It's time to keep alert for the frogs. In the fall the biggest ones will be gathering along the rock-free channels, where there is the most soft mud to burrow into for winter. They'll be frightened by the coming bullboat and jump for shelter. Paddle the bullboat into those passages where you hear the loudest, funniest croaks and the biggest splashes.

In this way you'll reach the wide willow wallow where cattle, having pushed down the pasture fence (F), have come down into the boggy willows to shade themselves from face flies, to drown their heel flies and to rub others off on branches. They push low, complicated tunnels through the tall, thick willows, and some of their tunnels will lead to a hummocky marsh (G) where stagnant hoofprint puddles have bred millions of waiting mosquitoes.

Now sing as you paddle, to keep from suddenly spooking the cattle you meet, and reach carefully from the bullboat for the fruit of the highbush cranberries that grow amid the willows. The closer you get to the open hummocky marsh edges, the less acid is the soil and the sweeter the berries, so pay attention to your taste and travel only through tunnels where your lunch stays refreshingly tart, and there will be fewer mosquitoes.

You will emerge into a long, wide slough
(H) leading to the ducks' dominion. Here
there are dabbling ponds so shallow that even
the bullboat would get stuck in the soft, oozy
mud that no one can walk out through. But
there are also diving ponds that you can paddle
through freely. Keep your eyes on the circus
of ducks.

If you can find shovelers alone on a pond, with their long, wide bills, playing follow-the-leader, you'll know it's a shallows to dodge. If you can find ringnecks and redheads alone, suddenly showing at a pond's surface with beaks full of strange green weeds, you'll know here's some deeps to head for. But the bald-pates, gadwalls and green-winged teals will more than likely be there, too, tipping tails up and heads down, squabbling among themselves, dabbling for feed in the shallows and snatching weeds right from the divers' beaks where they surface. They'll be making busy, splashing contests in every pond, and because in the summer and early fall all ducks have the same sort of brownish feathers, you'll have to get very close to tell in which ponds the diving ringnecks and redheads really are.

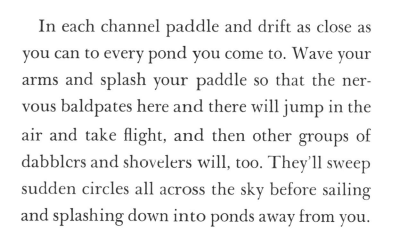

In each channel paddle and drift as close as you can to every pond you come to. Wave your arms and splash your paddle so that the nervous baldpates here and there will jump in the air and take flight, and then other groups of dabblers and shovelers will, too. They'll sweep sudden circles all across the sky before sailing and splashing down into ponds away from you.

The divers may just dive, or they will run and splatter across the water on their wingtips before rising into the air. Be ready to spot where those ducks start from, and they'll show you the different deeps across the whole dominion, till you come to the last single channel. It leads to the egg eddies (I) and the butterfly bends (J).

You'll feel the water speed up as it narrows all at once. You'll feel the warmth of warm springs flowing out from beneath the steep mudbanks, and you'll see how these springs, at every bend, freshen and clean the water that the cows have manured and the ducks have muddied. You'll see how the inflows from the springs have pushed light floating materials into the eddies opposite each bend.

Hundreds of hatched eggshells will be caught in the mudbank of every eddy: the speckled purple and white of the larks, the blue-green of the robins, the creamy tan and olive colors of duck eggs, all washed down and left by the high waters of springtime. Stuck in below the eggs, and glowing gaily, will be the bright feathers shed by the male ducks during the lower water of early summer: green, red, white, black, and blue feathers, large and small, fluffy and smooth. And on the bent walls, right across the eddies, migrating monarch butterflies will be clinging and resting like living curtains of orange and black, gently waving in the warmth rising from the warm springs. Since the water has its own push, and there are no wrong turns the bull-

boat can make, there's nothing for you to do but sail along, in and around and out of the eddies and on your way, resting, relaxing and looking.

You will come, after awhile, to the corn crop curve. Here you must stop, for you can't depend on guides through the ribbon routes of the fog forest until evening.

Now you may as well eat something sweeter and more solid than cranberries. Above the corn crop curve there is a dry, open slope (K)

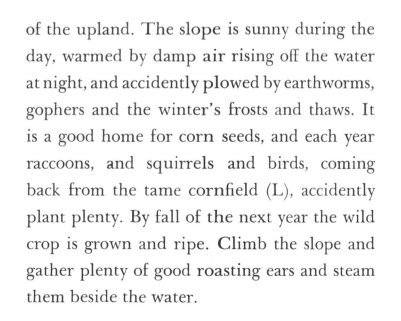

of the upland. The slope is sunny during the day, warmed by damp air rising off the water at night, and accidently plowed by earthworms, gophers and the winter's frosts and thaws. It is a good home for corn seeds, and each year raccoons, and squirrels and birds, coming back from the tame cornfield (L), accidently plant plenty. By fall of the next year the wild crop is grown and ripe. Climb the slope and gather plenty of good roasting ears and steam them beside the water.

You'll notice the steam fog in the forest beside you getting thicker, too. It's the mixing of the water warmed by the warm springs with the cool, shaded air of the forest that causes this fog. It gets thicker as the cooling air from the uplands starts sliding down the deep gully at evening. Then—done eating or not—you must be ready to leave, just before dark. That is the only time you can be sure of finding the kingfisher resting at the opening of his high mudbank burrow (M). Get carefully back in the round bullboat and *steer left* as it drifts into the fogbound first forks of the forest.

If you go at the right time there'll be just enough light for the kingfisher to see you, and he'll fly off with a darting flutter of blue so bright that for a moment it's visible through the fog, though so quick you might miss it. Yet you're sure to hear him scolding away with a clear, rattling call.

Bear right! into the fog when you hear that call and you will pass onto the proper ribbon route. You'll have to start paddling steadily again, now, for the water will be spreading through the routes and slowing down. The raccoons will be getting ready to leave their hollow tree (N) and will hear your paddles. Their sentinel will begin crying, "Scroo-oorp-oorp-oorp, scro-oorp-oorp-oorp," shrilly until you are past. *Bear left!* when you hear her start, then remember to *bear right!* when she stops.

Now you must slow down and stop and be very still and patient. You may hear an owl hoot at any time in the forest. Don't pay any attention to the owl, for he can see no better than you in the fog, and you can't depend on where he will be.

You must stay still till you hear the ringing squawks of the great blue herons in their nests in a big sycamore tree (O). Sound carries well in moist air, and when they dream or wake up and call out or complain occasionally, you will

N

hear them. By moving then, and stopping the moment you've lost the sense of their direction until you hear them again, you'll be able

to paddle forward and avoid making a wrong turn into the log-locked lagoon (P) where tangled dead limbs and trunks make it impossible to pass.

When a startled, honking squawk tells you the heron nests are directly above you, *bear left!* or you will go into a dead end.

After turning left and groping aways along the banks you will see (Q) the first glow from the swamp fire. Some swamp fires seem to bounce through the trees, but others, like the one in the fog forest, burn with a steady light. What swamp fire is, no one really knows, but perhaps it is gas escaping from decaying plants, and flaming in the air. You will have to paddle right toward it, or you might go by mistake into the other openings of the log-locked lagoon. You will have to paddle right through the swamp fire. It will not hurt. It glows all around you but burns at a very cool temperature. On the other side you'll suddenly see a channel of stars shining clearly above you, and over the river that will be directly in front of you.

Then if you paddle on only a short distance against the push of the river's current, you will come to the cove, and your canoe, and to your bed within your tent. You will have had enough of being a river pilot for awhile, and will be ready, perhaps, to be a story teller, telling the kind of stories only river pilots can tell.